R. S.
Agency, Ia. - 1902

ECLECTIC SCHOOL READINGS

TEN COMMON TREES

BY

SUSAN STOKES,

Department of Biology, High School, Salt Lake City.

NEW YORK ∴ CINCINNATI ∴ CHICAGO

AMERICAN BOOK COMPANY

PREFACE.

Most of us have a general idea of what trees are, but few have real acquaintance with them.

It is hoped that the following pages will lead to a number of simple nature lessons on trees and result in more definite impressions of what they are and how they live.

Leaves and fruits are best adapted for these lessons; the flowers are often too complex. The teacher should provide leafy twigs and the fruits, and can easily obtain from the children simple descriptions of them. A description of the leaf should include its position, the arrangement (opposite or alternate), size, shape, color, time of appearance and use. The fruits may be treated in a similar way. The description should be accompanied by a simple drawing of leaf or fruit. This makes vivid the impression upon the child's mind and gives to the lesson an invaluable touch of reality.

The substance of the material in this book, first appeared as a series of articles in Primary Education. The drawings were made by Mr. E. H. Estmond.

CONTENTS.

TEN COMMON TREES.

BLACK WILLOW.

It was one cold morning in March.

Black Willow looked down on her cousin Pussy, who grew in the shade of her branches, and said:

"Pussy, Pussy, what have you done? You have taken the scales from your winter buds. This wind is as cold as can be."

Now, Pussy was just a shrub, not nearly so old as the big tree by her side; she had a dozen or more branches coming from near the ground all together, while the big tree had one big trunk, about two feet around. But she did not feel cold, so she said:

"I am not cold. Just see the gray wool with which my buds are covered. That will protect my flowers from the cold, and as for my leaves, they will not be out for some time to come."

Fig. 1. Pussy Willows.

Black Willow saw that the shrubby willow was covered with short, furry stems, like the tip of a kitten's tail (Fig. 1), but that no leaves were to be seen.

This was strange, for Black Willow was not accustomed to show her catkins until the leaves were also ready. Not until then did she drop the single brown hood from her winter buds (Fig. 2).

"It's better to wait until later," she said.

" My flowers get all the sunshine this way," was Pussy's reply, "and my seed children have a nice start before fall."

In spite of what Pussy had said, Black Willow found April a better time to begin. She had always waited for the south wind to come. Then,

> Showers of rain fall warm and welcome,
> Plants lift up their heads rejoicing,
> Back unto their lakes and marshes
> Come the wild goose and the heron,
> Homeward shoots the arrowy swallow,
> Sings the bluebird and the robin,
>
> *　　　*　　　*　　　*　　　*　　　*
>
> All the meadows wave with blossoms,
> All the woodlands ring with music,
> All the trees are dark with foliage.

If Pussy were right then the pussy willows ought to live to be old as the black willows do. But there are very few of them that

2. WINTER BUDS. are strong enough to develop even into small trees.

Black willows live a long time, they grow tall and have long drooping branches high above the heads of the pussy willows.

So Black Willow drew a quantity of water up into her trunk and twigs. Her roots went down under the stream which was filled with melting snows.

One day when the sun was warm the flat brown hoods covering her buds slipped off and some scaly catkins pushed out. They were covered with tiny green scales fitting over one another like the shingles on a roof. There were some small leaves below; the twigs were not red as Pussy's had been and the catkins were scarcely furry at all (Fig. 3).

4. THE STAMINATE CATKIN.

When these were a little older the scales pulled apart, and a sweet odor was carried by the breeze all around. The bees came looking everywhere for the honey. And where do you think they found it? Under the green scales.

3. CATKINS OF BLACK WILLOW.

They had just been across the stream to another willow. It looked exactly like our tree but for its flowers. The catkins

5. SINGLE SCALE WITH STAMEN.

on that tree were bright yellow and numbers of little yellow balls stood out from under its scales. Those balls had been covered with a bright gold-colored dust called pollen (Figures 4 and 5).

The bees had put a little of the pollen into some baskets on their hind legs. Then they sipped the honey at the base of the scale and started off to find some more.

They traced the sweet odor to our Black Willow on the

6. PISTILLATE CATKIN.

other side of the stream, and found the honey under the scales of the catkins (Fig. 6). But they did not find any of the golden dust which they liked to carry home to feed to the bee babies.

Instead of the stamens with their yellow anthers, they found a tiny green bottle, with a sticky summit which is called a *stigma* (Fig. 7).

They crawled all over the catkin, their dusty legs brushed against the sticky stigma and some of the golden dust stuck fast. But that was right, for the tree on the other side had sent the pollen to our tree and had paid the bee

7. SINGLE SCALE WITH PISTIL.

with honey for carrying it.

Would you like to know what Black Willow does with this gold dust?

It uses it to help make seed. Down in the bottom of each green bottle, or *pistil*, there are some very young seeds waiting to grow, and after they get the pollen they do grow.

On the inside of each seed is a willow baby. It is a very tiny baby, but the mother tree has given it a little jacket with a tuft of down.

There are a great many of these babies in jackets

8. CATKIN WITH MATURE PISTILS.

in the green pistil, and to hold them all as they grow, it gets bigger and bigger, until by and by it bursts and the downy seeds pop out (Fig. 8). The wind catches them and away they fly.

Some of the willow babies did not reach the ground; they were carried off by a yellow bird that was building in the tree across the stream, and were used to make a soft and downy lining for the young birds' nest.

Although Pussy Willow had bloomed so much earlier than Black Willow, her leaves were not out much sooner. Black Willow unfolded hers at the same time that the catkins were lengthening. The two were alike in a great many ways.

They were of about the same size and shape with very many delicate veins forming a network. They also grew in alternate order, that is, there was one on one side and then one on the other side of the stem. Black Willow's were longer and narrower than Pussy Willow's and they tapered to both ends (Fig. 10).

At the base of each leaf just where it joined the stem were usually two black dots. These marked the place from which the *stipules* fell.

The stipules look quite different in different parts of the tree. On the later shoots that spring from near the ground they are often large and form two leaflike ears on either side of the base of the leaf (Fig. 9).

9. STIPULES ON YOUNG SHOOTS.

On the later branches they are often so small that you might think they were not there at all. In these cases they are small and hairlike and fall early, leaving a small scar.

Willow leaves are so much alike that you must look very closely if you would tell which willow you

have. Some of them have smooth edges, and some
of them have tiny teeth.

Black Willow has the toothed margin and its

10. LEAF OF BLACK WILLOW.

under surface is silvery. There is a vein near the
margin which runs all the way around.

The leaves are used to make food. They have a
heavy coat on the upper side to shed the rain and
prevent the leaf from drying out when the sun shines
upon it.

This coat is so tough that it is necessary to have
places where the air can get through. The gateways
are small openings through the *cuticle* or wall.
There is a guard
cell on either side,
and they are
found on the un-
der side of the leaf.
They are so very
tiny that we use
a powerful lens
to study them.

11. BREATHING PORES IN UNDER SIDE OF LEAF.

Through these pores the air passes in and the
water which the tree no longer needs is thrown off.
They are called "breathing pores" (Fig. 11).

Willows drink a large amount of water. For this reason they live on the banks of streams, where their roots help to hold the soil when the melting snows fill the stream and threaten to wash everything away.

They also are frequently found in soils which hold a large amount of water. Much of it is drawn into the tree and thrown off through the leaves. This helps to make new clouds.

Black willows are often planted in parks along sidewalks, and they grow in all parts of the United States. The western form differs slightly from the eastern. Both have rough dark bark and the leaf stem, or *petiole*, is smooth.

You must not think that the black willow is the only tree willow.

The white willow is another. It has yellow twigs, and silvery white or gray leaves. The leaf petioles are somewhat spotted with little bodies called glands.

The crack willow is a tall tree with very brittle twigs. The young leaves are green above and waxy beneath.

The poplars and cottonwoods are near relatives of the willows. The leaves are much broader, and the buds better protected. The staminate flowers are less crowded. Some day you may compare them with the willow.

A tiny gall gnat sometimes sting the ends of the twigs and stems of willows. This causes them to swell, and the buds instead of growing into twigs, form leafy cones which might be mistaken for the fruit. The young of the gnat develop in these cones.

The shoots of many willows are grown for basket work. They are planted close and when they have grown tall and slim they are cut. The bark is then stripped off and the wood used in the making of baskets and chairs.

References:

Under the Willows. Lowell.
The Trees. Larcom.
The South Wind and the Sun. Riley.

THE AMERICAN ELM.

Did you ever think what a fine old teacher Winter is?

You would like to be in his school, I know, for he teaches such interesting things.

There are clouds learning to snow, brooks building roofs, partridges coloring their feathers, and bluebirds being sent south. There are oaks and elms learning how not to be cold, and pines thickening their needles.

How does he do it?

He began with our elm when it was only a straight, slim wand growing in the rich soil of a meadow. He came around in the early fall.

The elm still had its pretty green leaves. He said, "Listen to me. I shall be coming soon. You should cover the ends of your twigs. It will soon be too cold for them."

The little elm heard, and stretched the scales around the bud so that they covered it all over. Where two came together, it put another over the place.

You can see what they looked like in the figures on page 17.

Winter came again, with a colder snap than before. This time he said, "You should drop your leaves, it will be warmer without them."

And again the little elm heard and it dropped its leaves and found it warmer without.

When Winter finally came to stay he could not get in, for the doors were safely barred. So he said, "Well done. That is the way they ought to be."

There were others that did not do so well and with them he was severe. He nipped the ends of their twigs so that they did not grow again. That is the way trees are made hardy. Only the strongest can live.

It is really very strange that a slender twig, scarcely larger than a straw, can keep alive in weather that will freeze a foot of ice on the pond. There are very many that do not. A large number do not survive the first year.

All winter long the little elm was just as still as could be. It rested and waited until the days grew longer and the nights were not very cold.

Then the sap began to flow. The twigs back of the buds filled up. The warm sun shone and the elm loosened the scales a little. Then the leaves came out.

1. WINTER TWIG.
2. BUD SHOWING SCALES ABOUT THE GROWING POINTS.

They were of a pale gray color, folded and plaited, and covered with down. The veins ran from the midrib to the margin very evenly.

These leaves grew longer and wider, they had a pointed tip and a saw-toothed edge. The leaf stem, or *petiole*, was quite short, and one half of the oval blade was smaller than the other. They were about three inches long.

The twigs and buds were bare and smooth, and the early leaf down was soon shed. The leaves

spread out on either side of the stem like a feather.

In this way the little elm showed that it was a white or American elm. Later its branches spread out like a great vase, and that is also

3. ELM TWIG SHOWING FEATHER-LIKE ARRANGEMENT.

a feature of the American elm.

All summer long it kept on growing. It pushed out its tip and added leaves, first one on one side of the stem, and then one on the other. It started some twigs from the angles of last year's leaves and looked much more like a tree than it had the year before.

When winter came the elm had a stout heart and a warm bark. It made winter buds through which the frost could not pierce. Then, too, it was in a sheltered place and the wind did not sweep through its branches.

In this way it grew. In the spring it stretched its twigs into long branches. The rains washed it, the winds fanned it, and the earth fed it. And it became a tall, slender tree, with graceful, spreading arms.

When the elm was several years old it flowered for the first time. It was in April, when Spring

4. FLOWERING TWIG.

> Cometh over the hills,
> Her garments with morning sweet,
> The breath of a thousand rills
> Making music before her feet.

This year, when the buds opened, it was not leaves that came out, but purplish tufts of tiny bells (Fig. 4). Some of the bells had several clappers apiece, some of them had none, but had instead two hairy arms, purple in color. Some of them had both (Figures 5 and 6). These were the flowers of the elm.

5. STAMINATE FLOWER.

6. PISTILLATE FLOWER.

The purplish cup, or bell, was the cloak or *calyx;* the clappers, the *anthers* filled with golden pollen dust; the hairy arms were the *stigmas* held up to catch the pollen borne by the wind from another tree.

People who have studied plants and trees for many years have found that the seed which grow when the flower uses its own pollen are weaker than the seed which grow when the pollen comes from another plant of the same kind and not from the flower's own anthers.

They think that is the reason the elm flowers before the leaves come out. Can you see that the

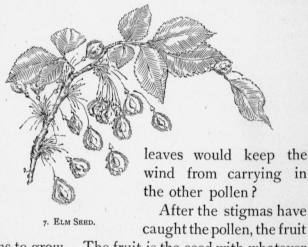

leaves would keep the wind from carrying in the other pollen?

After the stigmas have caught the pollen, the fruit

7. ELM SEED.

begins to grow. The fruit is the seed with whatever cloak may be wrapped about them. In the elm this cloak is flat and round and green.

It looks like a green leaf with a notch in the outer end and a fringe of hairs around the edge (Fig. 7).

The tiny cup of the flower is just below it, and the slender *pedicel* is about an inch long. In the center is a thickened part. Within this is the seed, and in the seed is the baby elm.

Now, can you tell me why it should have a wing, a sail? It is that the wind may carry it away and plant it outside the shade of the mother tree.

The white elms are among the most beautiful of the forest trees. They are often planted along streets, and their long branches meeting overhead form arches. There are several such streets in New Haven, which is called the "City of Elms."

There are also many historic elms. The Washington Elm at Cambridge, and the old elm at Pittsfield, Massachusetts, are two of these.

There is another near Philadelphia, known as "Penn's Treaty Elm." Why, do you think, did it receive that name?

A long time ago, before the Druids chose to worship only the oak, people would plant "birth trees" when a child was born, and the tree became a sort of household god. It was thought that bad luck would come to the child if anything happened to the tree.

The elm was one of the favorite trees planted in this way. It was also planted in front of the churches. Almost all of the old churches in France have an elm so planted. The people thought that they brought good luck.

There are other elm trees, which are somewhat like the white elm. You may know them by their alternate leaves, one side of which is smaller than the other, and by the veins which stand out like branching ridges. They have also a round, flat, winged fruit.

8. TWIG OF CORK ELM.

One of these is the red elm or slippery elm, which grows in rich soil on river banks or hillsides, but is also planted in cities.

It looks as if it had once lived in a colder place, for its bud scales are lined with rusty wool, its flowers and seed are woolly, and even its twigs are downy. The leaves are from four to eight inches long. The inner bark is sticky when wet, giving it the name " slippery elm."

Some have a very thick, corky bark. The cork elm is of this kind. Its branches are not smooth and round, but swell out in strange irregular shapes (Fig. 8).

9. TWIG OF WINGED ELM.

The winged elm has the cork arranged as a wing on either side of the stem. Its leaves are much shorter than those of the other elms.

You will also find a great many Scotch and English elms. Neither of these are tall and erect like the American elm.

The Scotch elm has spreading or drooping branches. The fruit has a shallow notch. It is not a native though frequently planted.

The English elm is hardly so flat-topped as the last, but it branches more abruptly than the American elm. Its leaves are much smaller and of a darker color.

If you look closely at an elm, you will find that it has insect guests. Some of them may be fat little grubs, with white bodies, black dots, and a black stripe; these are later transformed into white and green leaf beetles.

The canker worms are of several colors, but each has a yellowish stripe on the side and two white bands on the head; they often eat the tree quite bare. There are also some very large green caterpillars with sawlike teeth down the back and white lines on the sides. These become hawk moths, later. In the fall, elms are subject to the attacks of web worms.

The birds are a protection against the insects, and are, on this account, friends of the trees. The Baltimore oriole is especially fond of the elm, and its hanging nest is more often seen in that tree than in others.

References:

Hail to the Elm.   W. S. Dodge.

Autocrat of the Breakfast Table.   Holmes.   (Historic Elms.)

Among the Trees.   Brackett.   Harper's Magazine, September, 1896.

THE APPLE TREE.

Have you plucked the apple blossoms in the spring?
In the spring?
And caught their subtle odors in the spring?
Pink buds pouting at the light,
Crumpled petals baby white,
Just to touch them a delight —
In the spring?
—*William Martin.*

If you live in a large city, you may not know the
apple tree. In winter
it is a short reddish
tree, with a flat or
rounded top. Its stout
thick branches are
irregular and rigid.

In spring it is a
white tree. Its large
clusters of white and
pink flowers look like
short stemmed bouquets with a margin of leaves below.

In the fall it is a green tree. That is the season we
like it best for then it bears its apples of red and gold.

The poet Bryant has written the following upon
planting the apple tree. He says:

What plant we in the apple tree?
Buds which the breath of summer days
Shall lengthen into leafy spray;
Boughs where the thrush with crimson breast
Shall haunt, and sing, and hide her nest;

We plant, upon the sunny lea,
A shadow for the noontide hour,
A shelter from the summer shower,
When we plant the apple tree.

I will show you first its twigs. They are marked with the scars of last year's leaves. Just where they join the branch are some circular scars, very close together. They mark the place of last year's bud scales (Figures 1 and 2).

Last year it grew from the circular scars to the bud. If you look

1. TWIG OF APPLE

farther back on the stem, you will find some more scars like these. Each set marks the place of a winter bud, and you can tell the age of the branch by counting from winter bud to winter bud, a year for each space.

The buds are of two kinds, leaf buds and flower buds. The leaf buds are usually single, the flower buds in clusters. They are no larger than the stem. The scales cover the end of the twig.

2. WINTER BUD OF APPLE.

They are short scales, and around the edge of each is soft, fine wool to keep the tender, inner part warm. The twigs also are downy.

With the warm air come the

> Apple blossoms, budding, blowing,
> In the soft May air;
> Cups with sunshine overflowing —
> Flakes of fragrance, drifting, snowing,
> Showering everywhere !

Let us see what these flowers can tell us. They will speak to our eyes not our ears (Fig. 3).

Here is a flower. It says, "I have a round white face. I have a yellow center. Look behind and you will see that I am attached to the tree by a slender stalk. Where it joins the flower it is thick and round like a bud."

The calyx will say, "I am the outside part of my flower. I help to keep it warm. I have five green sepals covered with down. They are closed over the whole flower in the bud."

3. APPLE BLOSSOMS.

"My petals help, too," says the corolla. "They keep the stamens and pistils warm in the bud and tell the bees where to come for honey. They are broad and white on the inside, but red as a rose on the outside."

And then the stamens. "We stand in a circle. There are about thirty of us. Each of us has a slender body and a yellow head. The head is full of pollen. What is pollen? Pollen is a yellow powder which helps to make the seed grow."

Just in the center are five green arms with sticky tips. What can they tell us?

4. CROSS SECTION OF BASE OF APPLE BLOS-SOM.

"We catch the pollen. We are part of the pistil. The pistil holds the seed. Where? Down under the flower. It has five little rooms. In each are some very young seeds, which will grow when they get the pollen (Figures 4 and 5).

Down at the base of the stamens and style there is some honey for the bees. The bees visit the trees for this honey, bringing in pollen from other flowers and taking some away. In this way the flowers do not always use their own pollen.

5. VERTICAL SEC-TION OF APPLE BLOSSOM.

But I think the leaf tells the best story of all. This is what it says:

"All winter long I lived in the bud. There were a great many of us, and we were so closely packed that it was warm and cozy. One day the scales about us loosened, and a whiff of fresh air reached us.

"It was so good we all crowded out and stretched into the light. Then I found out what I was like. I had a broad green blade, a slender stem, and at the base of that two little ears, *stipules*.

"My blade was fine and crisp, for it had a great many veins to hold it out. One, in the middle was the *midrib* and there were several to each side.

"Did you know that these veins bring me water from the ground? I use the water and make starch and sugar. Then I send some of the sugar back to the roots in return for the water they send me. They are always in the ground and never get out to look at the sun or feel the wind. If the leaves did not send them food they would starve. We make the food in the apple, too.

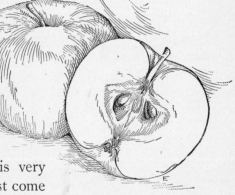

"The wind is very cold when I first come out, so the underside

6. APPLES.

of my blade is covered with yellow wool. That keeps the cold air from entering at my *breathing holes*. Leaves need air just as you do, and they take it in through tiny holes on the under side of the leaf."

After the pollen falls upon the sticky *stigmas*, the round part, below the flower begins to grow, and it grows into an apple, but you know apples so well that you will be able to tell me all about them.

They have a smooth skin, and are sunk at both ends. The stem is at one end and the remains of the calyx at the other (Fig. 6). There are still five rooms in the center with the seed.

The walls of the rooms are tough, and the mother tree has stored away a lot of food between these walls and the skin. You see the apple is intended to be a winter home for the seed.

When spring comes the apples have become soft and the seed have a nice place to begin to grow. Wild apples do not have so much food stored in the wall.

The food also attracts birds, so that they carry the seed away.

Each seed contains a baby apple tree, and has a brown and shiny coat. You do not find the tree? The hard white kernel is the young tree. How do we know? By the fact that the kernel swells up and grows into a little tree.

The coat cracks and the two leaves are pushed out while the short stem is lengthened into a root. The young plant packed away in the seed is called an *embryo*.

Shall I tell you the story of some wonderful apples, the apples of the Garden of Eden?

There was once a beautiful garden. It was away to the east. All sorts of fruits and flowers grew in this garden. And there lived in it a man, Adam, and his wife.

There was one tree, of the fruit of which they were forbidden to eat. If they did they would surely die. It stood in the middle of the garden.

There was also in the garden a beautiful but an evil serpent. It told Eve that if she ate she would not die but would be as the gods were, knowing good from evil.

Then Eve ate of the fruit and Adam also ate and they knew good from evil.

But The One who had placed them in the garden was angry and drove them forth, and "He placed at the east of the garden of Eden cherubim and a flaming sword which turned every way to keep the way of the tree of life."

Up in Norway and Iceland there is told the story of Iduna and her golden apples.

Iduna was a beautiful goddess who had charge of some wonderful apples, apples that made all who ate of them young and happy. The gods ate of these apples, and remained young and the earth was always green.

But there was one, the evil god, Loki, who thought he would like to see the world grow cold and old. He persuaded Iduna to go with him to see some wonderful apples that grew outside the city gate.

There she was stolen away by a giant from Jötunheim. Then the world grew cold and the gods grew gray. They mourned for Iduna.

"If you do not bring her back we will kill you," said they to Loki.

So he went to the home of the giant and rescued her.

When Iduna came back, winter was driven away. The gods ate once more of the golden apples and grew young; the earth was fair and the flowers bloomed again.

When the children of Greece lay in the shade, resting from their games, they were told the story of the golden apples of Hesperides.

Hercules, the strong son of Jupiter, was commanded to bring them to his cousin, whom he served. The apples had been given to Here, the queen of heaven, at the time of her marriage to Zeus.

They were guarded by the daughters of Atlas, he who bore the weight of the heavens on his shoulders. Hercules sought them far and wide. At last he came to Atlas in Africa.

He thought that Atlas must know where they were if any one did, so he sent him to seek the apples, and took upon his own shoulders the burden. This was one of the "seven labors of Hercules."

You observed that the apple is a fleshy fruit with the seed in horny cavities. Such a fruit is called a *pome*.

There are other fleshy fruits which have a single bony stone in the center, like the peach and cherry. They are then called *drupes*.

The nearest relatives of the apple bear pomes, many of the others bear drupes. In this way we can divide them into two groups. Those which bear pomes are the pear, quince, and crab apple.

The wild crab apple tree is small and has beautiful pink blossoms. The fruit is small and sour; it is sunken at both ends, and is about an inch in diameter.

The pear tree differs from the apple tree in not being flat-topped, and in being taller than broad. The flowers are white with purple anthers, and are without scent.

7. COUSINS OF THE APPLE.

The pears are sunken at one end only, and the stem end is smaller. The trees are often thorny.

The quince tree has broader leaves; the flowers are not in clusters but solitary, and of a white or rose color. The large yellow fruit is hard and sour, and is sunken at the flower end (Fig. 8). There are many seeds in each cavity and these become covered with jelly when soaked in water. The tree has a crooked stem with rambling branches.

The trees which bear drupes are the peach, plum, and cherry.

Peach trees are

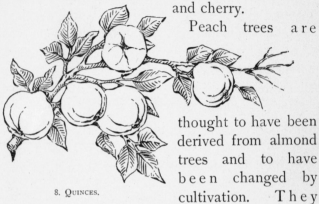

8. QUINCES.

thought to have been derived from almond trees and to have been changed by cultivation. They bloom early,

Ere ever the first bee hummeth,
Or woodland wild flower blows.

9. SECTION OF PEACH BLOSSOM.

They have large pink flowers, long narrow leaves, a downy fruit, and a wrinkled stone.

The plum trees usually have smaller flowers and the fruit has a bloom, that is, a thin wax coat which can be rubbed off. The stone is flattened. The trees are often thorny.

The pistil is single, with a single room in the lower part. This is also the case with the cherry and plum (Fig. 9).

Cherry trees have smooth fruits without bloom, and with a roundish stone. The cherries are borne in umbels, or in racemes, that is, on an elongated axis.

For cherry blossoms Japan surpasses all other places. The cherry trees are cultivated for the flowers, and when the trees are in bloom, people go long distances to see the finest groves. It is called the "Festival of the Cherry Blossoms."

Both the apple and the cherry have many cousins; one, which you know well, the wild rose, has given its name to the whole family. Look at this figure and see if you can tell why the apple belongs to the rose family (Fig. 10).

It is because it has broad petals, and many stamens, all of which are borne in a circle upon the green outer cup or *calyx*.

10. WILD ROSE.

Do you know of any family to which we owe more than to the rose family?

References:

The Wild Apples. Thoreau.
Peach Blossoms. Bayard Taylor.
Apple Blossoms. Lucy Larcom.
Planting of the Apple Tree. Bryant.

The Little Red-Apple Tree.   Riley.

Apple Blossoms.   Alice E. Allen.   Primary Education, May, 1899.

Three Trees.   Charles Crandall.   Primary Education, April, 1898.

THE HORSE–CHESTNUT.

Under the greenwood tree,
Who loves to lie with me,
And tune his merry note
Unto the sweet bird's throat.

The horse-chestnut is not an American tree. Shall I tell you how it comes to be here?

Long ago, you know, America belonged to the Indians. They built their wigwams, wore war paint and feathers, and wandered wherever they liked.

There were *native* plants and animals as well as native Indians, and they, too, spread everywhere over hill and vale. The beaver built in many brooks, and the wild grass perfumed the air. But when the Englishmen and the Frenchmen came over, they brought with them grains and fruits and domestic animals.

So the Indian pink and the wild flower were ploughed under, that the white man might have a wheat field; the "murmuring pines and the hemlocks" made way for apple and vine; and the tame duck swam in the wild-ducks' pools.

Now, only those trees are *native* which were growing here before the white men came. All the others are *introduced*. The horse-chestnut is one of these.

It is thought it came to Europe from Asia. There its nuts had been used as food for horses, as they still are in Turkey.

On this account, and because they look like the sweet brown chestnuts they are called "horse-chestnuts." In Southern Europe they are fed to sheep, cattle, and poultry; while in Ireland they are used in the bleaching of linen.

So you see the horse-chestnut may be a very useful tree, although in America it is more often planted simply as an ornament.

The horse-chestnut, like all the trees we have so far studied, drops its leaves in the fall and spends the winter in its trunk.

1. Section of Winter Bud.

When the cold wind howls outside, and says: "Ho! Ho! Are you there? Let me in," the tree says, "No! No! Don't you dare! You can't come in," and he can't, for how could he make his way through the rough, dark bark?

The gateways are through the winter buds, but the tree thought of that when he made the buds. He said to himself, " I'll get all my leaves ready to come out at once in the springtime (Fig. 1). But how shall I keep them from taking cold during the winter?"

So he thought and thought, and then he wrapped them all together in a thick coat of cotton and over the outside put, oh, so many scales! The inner ones were green, and the outer ones brown and shiny.

Said the tree to himself, " I'll coat them with resin so neither the snow nor the rain can get in." And he coated them over with shiny brown, and laughed to think how cosy they'd be.

Then he dropped the leaflets, one by one, and last of all the stem to which they had clung. On the brown branch where they fell were deep scars, shaped like a horse-shoe and with a row of dots around the edge like the nails of the shoe (Fig. 2). He went to sleep now " as snug as a bug in a rug," and waked only when the wind shook his head and threatened to tear him to pieces.

When Spring drew near, the warm south wind came softly and whispered in his ear, " Wake up, wake up, the robins are here ! "

2. TWIG OF HORSE-CHESTNUT.

So the horse-chestnut loosened his buds (Fig. 3), and spread them out more and more till only the last green cotton coverlid was left, then he cracked that, and what do you think he pushed through the crack ?

A cluster of tiny woolly hands, just as woolly as they could be, " softer'n a baby's be at three days old."

3. OPENING BUD.

Did he call them hands? Oh, no! He said, "These are my leaves. I made them last summer after my flowers fell." But they had five or seven fingers.

They were flat and were folded over and plaited together like a fan. When they spread out you found that they were broader near the tip than at the base (Fig. 4) and were very woolly underneath.

4. HORSE-CHESTNUT LEAF.

They came out very quickly, all at once, and turned the tree quite green in a single day. When these grew larger he didn't make even another one, but began at once to make ready for the next winter, making a new winter bud. It must be that is the reason it's so large, growing all summer long.

There was something else in the bud, just in the center, a great number of tiny green balls. They grew and grew and at last we knew they must be flower buds, but they were so long coming out They were not ready till June, the month when

Every clod feels a stir of might
　　An instinct within it that reaches and towers
And groping blindly above it for light,
　　Climbs to a soul in grass and flowers.

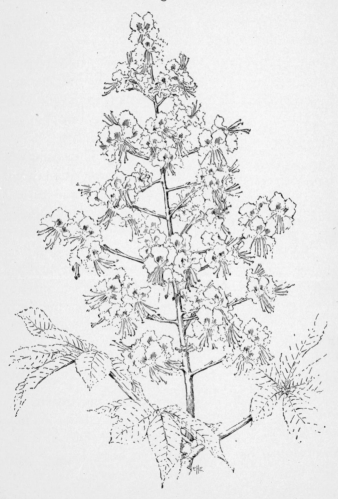

Out they came. Each separate branch was crowned with a great spire of buds, a giant nosegay. Some people even called it a "hyacinth tree" because its blossoms were so close and so fragrant (Page 41).

This great cone of flowers is called a *thyrsus*.

" The end flowers bloom first," said the tree, "and then the side buds push their way out beyond them, and take their turn in the sunlight. Of course, both my flowers and leaves must get the sunshine. Have you seen how my leaves peep out between each other, so that none are in the shade?"

But oh, the flowers! They were gorgeous. Each flower had a bright white party dress of its own.

On the outside there was first a little green cup. "Just a little spring jacket, you know, to be worn in the springtime." Inside of this was a dainty white dress, dotted with yellow and purple. It had five deep scallops on the edge. Even "Solomon in all his glory was not arrayed like one of these."

Of course everything that went by saw the beautiful white dresses and wondered what they were for, but the tree knew, for he had his invitations all ready for a great party.

He sent out a sweet odor on the breeze and every bee and bumble bee that passed knew that the tree was saying, "Come to see me. Come to see me. I have something for you. Come to see me. Here I am, over here, the tree with the white flowers."

And every one of them that received an invitation went at once. Each flew to a flower and put his tongue straight into a honey pot (Fig. 5).

How did he find it? On each one of those white petals, tiny lines and dots pointed to it and so the bee found it. They are called *insect guides*.

5. STRAIGHT INTO A HONEY POT.

"Do you see those stamens of mine?" said the tree. "They have pockets full of gold in their heads When the bees stood upon them, it jarred them a little and when they flew away they were just loaded with pollen dust." But the bee did not mind; he flew straight to another flower for

6. "A LITTLE GREEN BUD."

more honey. As he lighted there was a little green bud standing out from a circle of stamens which held their heads low (Fig. 6). It was the head of a pistil, and of course the bee bumped right into it. On he went after the honey, but the pistil was left crowned with the gold dust he carried.

7. STAMINATE FLOWER.

Then I looked closer and found that wherever the pistil held its head high, the stamens drooped

8 "The Petals Faded and Fell."

theirs, and when the pistil had been crowned for several days then the stamens lifted up their heads, opened their pockets and scattered the dust for some other flower.

"What's this," said I, "some of your flowers have no pistils?" "Oh, dear, no," said the tree, "if I had as many pistils as I have flowers I should be overloaded with burs in the fall."

I waited to see what this could mean, and until the petals faded and fell (Fig. 8) and the tree was full and green, a very dark green, with the broad leaf f a c e s spread out to the sun.

When I looked I found that the woolly pistil had been growing larger and larger and was covered over with short prickles.

9. Horse-chestnuts.

Later I saw it fall to the ground. A prickly bur it was be sure. Some cattle sniffed it, but not one was brave enough to try opening it.

" That's what the prickles are for," said the tree, and he really thought the ugly hooks were a pretty fine coat to make for his seed. As it lay on the ground the hard shell grew dry and then it popped open in three places, three doors to let out the shiny brown seed with its great eye. It looked so like the yellow-eyed chestnuts, that I was tempted to eat it, but I did-n't for I knew it was very bitter (Fig. 9).

Although the horse-chestnut is not a native of America it has some native cousins, which are called buckeyes. The Ohio buck-eye is well known. It has a very disagreeable odor. The leaves are opposite and palmate. There are

10. SWEET BUCKEYE.
a. LEAF; *b.* FLOWER;
c. BURS; *d.* NUT.

from five to seven leaflets, which are broadest near the middle and its burr is prickly. The greenish flowers are not so handsome as those of the horse-chestnut.

The yellow buckeye or sweet buckeye is so called be-cause it does not have the disagreeable odor common to the others. It grows from thirty to ninety feet high.

The leaflets are broadest near the middle, and the long, narrow flowers are yellow, with a deep green cup at the base. The bur is rough but not prickly (Figs. 10, *a*, *b*, *c*, and *d*).

References:

Sunthin' in a Pastoral Line.   Lowell.
The Horse-Chestnut.   Harper's Magazine, Vol. 74.
Fertilization of Flowers.   Miller.

THE BIRCH TREE.

At first it was only a tiny tree, with two little leaves lifted up to the light.

They were very little leaves, but they sifted the sunlight, made food for the roots and gave back to the clouds the water the roots had found in the soil.

Of course the sunlight helped them, and so when the breeze passed by they would sing in rustling voices "Oh sun, sun, beautiful sun!"

When the sun sank behind the hills in the west and the stars came out, the little tree went to sleep, and an owl in the great tree near by kept watch, saying " Hoo-hoo, Hoo-hoo!"

One morning the sky was gray and the rain fell in torrents. " Oh, what can the matter be, what is all this? " said the little tree.

" This? This is rain; we need it," said the big tree, and his leaves slip-slipped against each other. Then the sun came out and the leaves worked so busily that the little tree grew apace.

After a while, it grew so cold that the young tree shivered. "Why is it so cold?" it asked of the tall tree. "Winter is coming. Drop your leaves," said the great tree.

Then there came a gust of wind which carried away the young tree's leaves. "Oh, my leaves! my pretty leaves! Where are they going?" it cried.

But soon it found it was warmer without the leaves and so it did not regret them. Fortunately it was not very cold, there at the willow's feet.

When spring came again, it put out some more leaves. The bark upon the stem grew smooth and shiny and was marked with short horizontal lines, without any knots or uneven places. Near the tip it was downy, as is the way with birches.

One day a tall young Indian passed by. He was straight as an arrow and tall like the pine tree. He crossed over to a big tree, saying,

> Give me of your bark, O birch tree !
> Of your yellow bark, O birch tree !
> Growing by the rushing river,
> Tall and stately in the valley !
> I a light canoe will build me,
> Build a swift Chemaun for sailing,

That shall float upon the river,
Like a yellow leaf in autumn,
Like a yellow water lily!

Then the tree made answer,

Take my cloak, O Hiawatha!

Then Hiawatha stripped the tree of its smooth tough bark and "in the valley by the river," made his birch canoe and launched it.

Then he came again. This time

From his pouch he took his colors,
Took his paints of different colors,
On the smooth bark of a birch tree
Painted many shapes and figures.

Of course our young tree could not know their meaning, but it would have liked to have him put upon its bark some

Songs of war and songs of
  hunting.

Across the river from the little tree there stood a great birch tree. In the s p r i n g its branches were tipped with long d r o o p i n g tails, in the winter there were brown cones upon its bare boughs. The young birch wished to have some of these

1. WINTER BUDS.

2. PARTS OF BUD (MAGNIFIED). *a.* STAMENS WITH BRACTS; *b.* BRACT WITH STAMENS, SHOWING FILAMENT; *c.* LARGE OUTER BRACT, SIDE VIEW; *d.* BRACTS AND STAMENS, FROM BELOW.

3. CATKINS OF BIRCH. *a.* STAMINATE; *b.* PISTILLATE.

strange fruits, so it asked the old tree what it should do.

"You must begin in the fall," said the old tree, "make some long conelike winter buds. In the spring they will open and become these drooping yellow tails."

The young tree listened, and in the fall it made some great long buds (Fig. 1) and covered them over with thick scales (*bracts*.) Under each heavy scale, there were several thin scales. In each of these were two small balls full of yellow powder; they were fastened in place by a filament which forked (Fig. 2).

During April's sunny days the tail-like buds grew long and feathery, and the yellow pollen floated away. But still there were no black cones. Again the young tree asked, "What shall I do that I may have cones?"

The old tree replied, " Oh, you can make these in the spring.   Instead of making so many large leaves,

4. *a*, Bract from Pistillate Catkin; *b*, Pistils; *c*, Seed.

take some of your buds and do with them as I tell you."

So the young birch took some young twigs, such as it had been making into leaves.   On a stem not more than an inch long, (Fig. 3, *b*) it crowded almost a hundred tiny three-lobed bracts (Fig. 4, *a*). In front of each one were three little bodies, nearly round and quite flat for they were crowded.

5. Mature Cones.

These were the pistils. Each had two curved arms at the top.   They caught the yellow pollen dust which the wind carried about (Fig. 4, *b*).   It made them grow, not very large, but as large as the bract back of them (Fig. 4, *c*).

" What shall I do now ? " asked the young tree.

" Wait until winter, then shake them out and the
wind will carry them away and plant
them."

" What for ? "

" Have you forgotten that you
were once a tiny seed ? and that the
wind dropped you among the willows there? You fell from one of
my cones."

Was not the little tree glad to know
this ? glad to have been a part of that
great and beautiful tree ? Her cones

6. GRAY BIRCH. grew larger and thicker (Fig. 5), the little
seeds were strong and healthy, and when they were
ripe, the wind scattered them far and wide.

Would you like to be a birch tree and learn to
make soft catkins and winged seed ?

How may you tell the birches apart?
You must look at the bark, the leaves, and
the droop of the branches. They
are alike in their flowers and fruit.

Have you seen a tree with white
bark and long, hanging branches ?
A tree with branches so slender

7. EUROPEAN WHITE BIRCH. that they scarcely cast a shadow ?

This airy tree with its flicker of green and white
is a gray or white birch (Fig. 6). Its bark has

the horizontal markings peculiar to the birches. There are dark spots below the leaf scars, and the leaf is notched. The notches are not so deep, however, as those of its relative, the European white birch (Fig. 7).

The yellow birch is easily recognized by the yellow hue of the bark. But it was not from the bark of the yellow birch that canoes were made.

The paper or canoe birch has bark that easily separates in layers, and it was from this that the Indians made their canoes. The white color of the trunk is more conspicuous than that of the gray birch, but it lacks the brown patches, and the branches do not droop.

The white birch is not a tall tree; the paper birch frequently becomes tall, and its bark is unbroken for

8. PAPER BIRCH.

some distance upon the trunk. The leaf is shown in Figure 8.

The western birch, from which the drawings were taken, is a small tree, its twigs are very glandular, that is, they are rough and sticky. This character it shares with some of the eastern forms. The young stems are often downy.

The alders are closely related to the birches. The leaves and cones look much alike, the difference is in the stamens. The little stalk holding the anther is forked in the birches, but is distinct to the base in the alders.

References:

Song of Hiawatha.   Longfellow.
(*Hiawatha's Sailing.*)
Picture Writing.
The Birch Tree.   Lowell.
An Indian Summer Reverie.   Lowell.

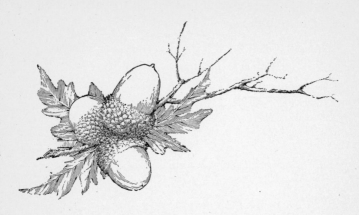

THE WHITE OAK.

What is a tree?   Is it only a wooden trunk with wooden branches, a bark and leaves?

There is something more.   Let me tell you about it to-day.   It's the *spirit* of the tree.   There is something about it, the shape of the head, the color of the leaves, the outline of the trunk which tells a tale.

The tree has an expression.   Elms toss their long branches and are dainty; birches are the "most shy and ladylike of trees."

What is the character of the oak?   The short trunk, holding its immense weight of branches says, "I am strong."   The great broad head of leaves says, "I am wise."   The whole tree seems to say "Trust me, you can depend upon me."   Its wood has shown the strength.

The heart of the oak has been used for hundreds of years in the building of ships and it will bear enormous strains.

> There needs no crown to mark the forest's king.

The poet Keats saw that they looked wise and dignified. He calls them

> Those green-rob'd senators of mighty woods.

If you had lived in England about two thousand years ago, you would probably have worshiped the oak trees. At that time there were there great forests of oaks and people saw in them such good qualities, they were so hardy, they wrestled like giants with wind and storm and lived to be so old that the people and their priests, the Druids, worshiped them.

In southern Europe about the same time, you would have been told about the Dryads, or maidens who lived in trees. Sometimes they were even seen. A young Greek returning from the chase would tell the tale:

"I started a stag on the mountain and followed him until I was weary. Then I threw myself on the ground beneath some great oak trees. I heard the lisping of the leaves and then a sweet voice singing; it sounded almost like the crooning of birds —

> Rest you, rest you,
> Green boughs shade you,
> Kind winds sing you,
> Soothe you, soothe you.

Sleep you, sleep you,
No bee hums near you,
No bird flits above you,
Dream you, dream you.

A DRYAD.

And then there slipped out of the trees some merry misty maidens, and they danced and danced. I half raised my head and they vanished like a flash."

So you see the Greeks also recognized the spirit of the tree. Some of the country people would even place food under the trees for the merry Dryads. Now-a-days we do not see the sprite that lives in the tree, but we examine her house very closely. If it's a white oak, we find a white trunk with a great dome-shaped roof.

This roof is upheld by stout many-curved arms and is covered over with leaves, bright green above and pale below. They have deep blunt notches and are arranged so that every leaf may get some sunshine (Fig. 1).

1. TWIG OF WHITE OAK. *a*, STAMINATE CATKIN; *b*, PEDUNCLES BEARING YOUNG CUPS.

The strangest thing about this roof is that it is used only in summer. In the fall it becomes a deep red. The twigs cover their tips with brown scales and begin to prepare new leaves for next summer's new roof.

The leaves then fall and the oak is ready for winter storms. These passed, the buds unfold and woolly pink leaves appear. With warm weather they turn green, and the oak's new roof is complete.

The oak bears two kinds of flow-ers on the same tree early in the year. The staminate flowers grow in catkins (Fig. 1, *a*). There are eight stamens in a tiny, many-lobed *calyx* (Fig. 2) and there are many flowers in the catkin.

2. STAMINATE FLOWER (MAGNIFIED).

The stamens provide the *pollen*. It is stored away in the two pockets of the *anthers*. These flowers are easily found in April or May.

The other kind, the pistillate flowers, will escape you if you are not careful. They do not look at all like flowers, but like tiny pink knobs (Fig. 1, *b*) on the tender young shoots.

3. PISTILLATE FLOWER (MAGNIFIED).

All you can see is three or four pink lips peep-ing out of a tiny cup (Fig. 3), the pol-len falls upon the lips, and both the cup and pistil within begin to grow. The pistil becomes the nut of the acorn and the cup becomes the cap of the nut (Fig. 4).

4. WHITE OAK ACORNS.

The cap is interesting for it repre-sents a branch of the tree, a branch which, instead of growing out and unfolding its leaves, has been kept short, and hardened that it might help to take care of the new oak, the baby that is to become a " lord of the forest."

For each one of her many acorn children the mother oak provides several things.

She makes it a cap from a twig, and a coat from the wall of the pistil. This horny coat keeps out the frost and the snow. In its two seed leaves she stores food enough to last through the winter and she gives it a tiny root so it has only to keep on growing.

The white oaks drop the acorns at the end of about six months, but the red oaks and black oaks do not shed their acorns until they are a year and a half old.

One windy day in October, an acorn fell from the top of a big white oak. It had been growing there since May.

At that time it had been so small that you could hardly have seen it at all. Still it held six little brothers, all together in the room at the bottom of the pistil. One of these had grown so fast that there was no room for the others, and at last it had the whole of the horny shell by itself. This was the baby oak of whose fortune I am going to tell you.

As it struck the ground its cap fell off and it rolled down a hill. On and on it went until it lodged in a little hole near the foot of the hill.

The wind which had started it, brought leaves and covered it over.

Here it was snug and quiet. Its cap was gone, but it had the hard brown coat which the mother tree had given it. There was a big round scar which showed where it had been broken off.

It lay under the leaves for a long time. It did not feel the cold, and it did not see the snow that covered the ground. But in the spring, the melting snow soaked through the little tree's hard jacket.

Then it awoke, and drank and drank, until the jacket actually cracked and split into three parts. Out through the rent crept a little root which turned and pushed down, down.

From between the two thick, white, seed leaves came a stem which grew up, but which kept its head bent over until it had pushed its way through the soil above.

It was a slender, reddish stem, with pairs of scaly leaves that did not look at all as leaves usually do.

5. BABY OAK.

After a while it began to have leaves that were like those of the white oak. They were no longer in pairs and were green in color.

These leaves made food which was carried to the root and helped to feed it. By this time all the food which had been stored in the seed leaves had been used (Fig. 5).

During the summer it grew to be a stout little tree. And in the fall it dropped its leaves and made ready for the winter. The next summer it grew again, and rested through the winter.

In this way it became strong and hardy, its branches thickened and the whole had a sturdy look. The winds blew upon it, but it did not bend. The snows loaded its branches, but it broke not. The hail pelted it and the clouds wept over it, and still it held its head to the storm and never weakened.

As it grew older it made flowers, and upon its branches were borne other acorns. The wild birds nested in its branches, the squirrels filled their stores from its fruits; the woodpeckers, also, carried the acorns away, digging little holes into which they put them for safe keeping.

The mistletoe clung to its branches, green even in winter time, and the ivy wound its slender stems about its trunk. So you see the little oak had become a power in the forest and repaid the care it had received.

6. BUR OAK.

SOME OF THE BEST KNOWN OAKS.

There are a great many different kinds of oaks. Would you like to be able to recognize a few of the common ones?

The flowers are all very closely alike. The leaves are not always the same on the same tree, but the acorns and acorn cups are so constant that we use them in distinguishing between the kinds.

7. BUR OAK ACORN.

October or November is the best time to study them. Look sharply when you go to the woods or to the park, and bring in a few leaves and a twig with some acorns. Be sure to find out at the same time if the acorns fall at the end of the first year, or at the end of the second. You will find the last on the tree during the winter.

Those which fall the first year are called annual fruited; they have usually a sweet kernel.

Those that fall the second year are called biennial fruited; they have a bitter kernel.

8. CHESTNUT OAK.

We will suppose your acorn is one of the first and has a sweet kernel. It may be either a white oak, a chestnut oak, or a live oak.

If it is either of the first two, the leaves will fall at the approach of winter, but if it is the last they do not.

The white oaks have very deeply notched leaves with blunt lobes, while

9. SWAMP WHITE OAK.

the chestnut oaks have large leaves with coarsely toothed or wavy margins.

10. *a*, Swamp White Oak; *b*, Scarlet Oak.

Now there are several kinds of white oaks and several chestnut oaks, but only one of each is called "white oak" or "chestnut oak."

The white oak which has received the name has a rough acorn cup, somewhat shorter than the acorn (Fig. 4). It is at its best in the Alleghany Mountains.

11. Southern Live Oak.

The mossy-cup white oak has a fringed and scaly cup which nearly covers the acorn. It is more abundant in the prairie region east of the Mississippi River. It is also known as the bur oak or over-cup oak (Figures 6 and 7).

The chestnut oak which receives the name has

12. Southern Live Oak.

leaves somewhat like the chestnut, but the teeth are not pointed (Fig. 8). Its acorns are borne on a stem shorter than the leaf stem or petiole.

The swamp white oak is classed with the chestnut oaks because the leaves are like those of the other chestnut oaks near the tip; they are, however, like the white oaks in being lobed near the base (Fig. 9). The acorns (Fig. 10, *a*), are born upon stems longer than the leaf stems.

The leaves of the live oaks are not deciduous, they are thick and heavy and the acorn cups taper to the peduncle or stem.

The southern live oak is a tree highly valued for its timber; the cups nearly cover the acorns (Figures 11 and 12).

The California live oak has long, slender nuts, sev-

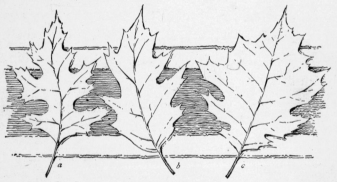

13. OAK LEAVES. *a*, SCARLET OAK; *b*, RED OAK; *c*. BLACK OAK.

eral times as long as the cups. The wood is brittle.

If you should have an acorn with a bitter kernel, it is probably a red oak, a black oak or a willow oak.

Red oaks have reddish wood. Their leaves are often deeply cut with the lobes tipped with bristles; they turn brilliant red in autumn.

The red oak has a shallow acorn cup, and the leaves turn orange-red in autumn (Fig. 13, *b*, and Fig. 14).

The scarlet oak has very ragged leaves, scarlet in autumn, the acorn cup is top-shaped, and rather deep; the kernel is white and bitter; the bark is gray without, red within (Fig. 13, *a*, and Fig. 10, *b*).

14. RED OAK.

The black oak is quite like the scarlet oak in many ways, but the bark is dark and rough, and has an orange-hued lining. This oak is valuable for the *tannin*, which is used in the manufacture of leather (Fig. 13, *c*).

The willow oaks have simple leaves like those of a willow, but very tough. The acorns are round like a ball.

References :

Germination of an Acorn. Prof. J. C. Arthur. Purdue University Leaflets.

Leaves and Acorns of our Common Oaks. Teacher's Leaflets, No. 8, Cornell University.

The Oak. Ward. (Modern Science Series.)

West American Oaks. E. L. Greene.

Last Dream of the Old Oak Tree. Hans Christian Andersen.

Baucis and Philemon. Myths of Old Greece.

Woodman, Spare that Tree. Morris.

The Oak. Lowell.

Rhoecus. Lowell.

Indian Summer Reverie. Lowell.

Myths of the Rhine. Saintine.

CHESTNUT TREES.

You have never hunted chestnuts?

Then you must go to the country some day in October. A day in the woods in October is something almost better than a day in June.

Some morning when the air is crisp and cool, when the frost is on the ground, put some apples and cookies in your pocket, and a long stick with a crook at the end over your shoulder.

1. CHESTNUT.

As you run across the hard white ground, you can shout and sing to your heart's content. You can pass the corn in shock, and tumble from the stack of straw. The chipmunk on the fence will listen to your whistle, and the red squirrel leap from tree to tree at your approach.

In the woods the maples will be scarlet, the ashes purple. There will be wintergreen berries with red jackets and white pulp. But you need not stop for these.

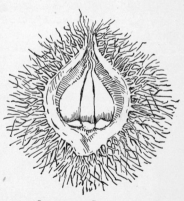

2. SECTION OF A CHESTNUT BUR.

Find the yellow tree with long leaves, saw-toothed on the edge. On the ground, scattered by last night's wind, are some long tailed nuts (Fig. 1) and some prickly burs (Fig. 2).

These burs are stiff and covered with sharp branched thorns. They open in four parts when tweaked by the frost (Fig. 3).

The wind helps pull them from the tree. If they should not have fallen, take your crook and shake them down.

3. "They Open in Four Parts."

When your pockets are full of chestnuts, when you have filled the salt sack you brought from home, when you have eaten apples with chestnuts, and chestnuts with cookies, you can hide your sack of nuts, while you explore a little.

You can climb the tree and peep at the gray squirrel's stock. He is a thrifty little fellow, for he puts by only the kernels. You would not think of robbing him.

The chipmunk, too, has a store, but they are underground. Once in a while, he puts a few together under some leaves; you may have found them.

4. Section of a Bur in July.

And then you can go home, home to pumpkin pie, and dreams of chestnuts popping in the ashes.

Here is a question for you. What are chestnuts?
Yes, chestnuts are seeds, but they are also young trees, each packed away in a tough brown coat.

Could you have looked in the bur in July, you would have found only some small white nuts (Fig. 4). In June they would have been so small

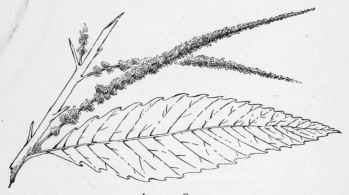

5. LEAF AND CATKINS.

that they were really not nuts at all but some long-necked flowers. Even then the three flowers had a prickly cup, or involucre.

I have told you about the oaks and the cap they make for the young acorn. This cup of the young chestnut is not very unlike the cap of the acorn. It grows much larger and it holds three flowers, instead of one, but it shows that the chestnut is a relative of the oaks.

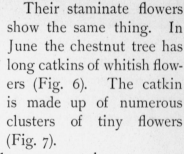

Their staminate flowers show the same thing. In June the chestnut tree has long catkins of whitish flowers (Fig. 6). The catkin is made up of numerous clusters of tiny flowers (Fig. 7).

The burs are not borne among these, but on separate peduncles as in the oak (Fig. 8).

7. "Clusters of Tiny Flowers." (Magnified).

Chestnut trees are known to live sometimes to an age of several hundred years. One on Mount Etna, in Italy, is a hundred and ninety feet around. It is called the "Tree of a Hundred Horses," for it once sheltered a queen with her followers. It is a Spanish or Italian chestnut. Other very old ones are found in England.

They do not differ materially from the American chestnut, but are frequently planted in America, for the nuts are larger. The American chestnut is smaller and sweeter.

The chestnut has some relatives, a little nearer than the oaks. They are the chinquapins.

The leaves of these are much smaller than the chestnut leaves.

8. A Young Bur.

The edge is only slightly toothed if at all, and the under surface is downy. The burs are smaller and there is but one nut instead of three. The nut is, of course, not flattened on the sides.

One of the chinquapins is a native of the Pacific coast, and is a tall tree. The other is southern, and the trees are quite small.

References :

The Chestnut Tree. Youth's Companion, Oct. 14, 1897.
In the Nutting Time. St. Nicholas, vol. XVII, 1894.
Two Sides of the Same Question. Chatterbox, 1892.
"Chestnut Time." Primary Education, Oct. 1898.

THE LITTLE WALNUT.

NCE upon a time there was a little nut. It lived in a green house upon the top of a high tree (Fig. 1).

The house was a sticky affair on the outside and had neither door nor windows. Still it was cosy and warm, for, as you see, it had a tough husk for an outer wall; next to this was a bony shell, and clear inside was the little nut (Fig. 2).

1. WALNUTS IN THE HUSK.

There were two rooms into which its two leaves fitted. Their walls were crumpled and the little nut pressed out just as far as it could and filled all the crannies.

This little nut was five months old, for it had arrived upon the tree in May. Now if you will look at a walnut tree in May, you will find it has made ready a great many homes for nut babies.

They don't look just like the full grown house, first, because they are not any larger than a grain of rice, and second, because they have two topknots. Perhaps we had better call them *chimneys*.

Here is a group of these nut houses (Fig. 3). You can find them in the tip of a branch just after the leaves unroll. The round part is sticky, but the chimneys are hairy and if you look very closely you can see that they have been dusted over with a yellow powder, and there is a slight frill at the neck (Fig. 4).

I have sometimes cut down into the house through the chimney and found where the grains had made their way through the chimney into a little room at the bottom.

In the little room was an egg cell. When the pollen grain reaches it, the little egg cell wakes up and begins to grow. It grows and grows until it becomes the kernel of a nut.

I think you would like to know where the little pollen grain, the walnut's Fairy Prince, came from. It was probably carried by the wind from another

2. SECTION OF WALNUT.

3. CLUSTER OF PISTILLATE FLOWERS.

4. A SINGLE FLOWER (MAGNIFIED).

tree, although we find both stamens and pistils on the same tree.

It came from a queer little flower, that has thirty or forty pockets full of gold dust. The little flower doesn't look much like a flower. It seems to be a little shelf holding eight or ten little stamens, each of which has four pockets (Fig. 5). The little shelves grow in clusters, in tail-like *catkins* (Fig. 6). There are from twenty to forty flowers in a catkin and a very great many catkins on a single tree.

5. SINGLE STAMINATE FLOWER (MAGNIFIED).

The catkins do not grow in the tip of the branch, but stand out from the sides farther back. They are always green in color and disappear after the wind carries away the pollen. They were very different from the little nuts high up in the tree. The little nuts kept on growing.

The winds rocked them to and fro, the rains washed their sticky walls, and the mother tree kept adding to the food supply in the little leaves.

By and by October came, and with it a high wind, which whisked our nut, house and all, down into a corner. But the same wind also carried the leaves about and covered the nut with a warm blanket. Then the clouds gathered and the white snow fell.

The little nut slept under the snow, but when the ground froze deep down, it cracked the nut's shell.

After a while the nut awoke and began to use the food the mother tree had put in its leaves. It was thirsty, too, and was glad to drink the melting snow. So it ate and drank and began to grow.

6. Young Leaves and Staminate Catkins.

The two rooms of its house became too small for it, and it pushed out a tiny root, which turned into the ground. By and by the little root was so busy getting water and the little nut was so busy using it, that a long green sprout sprang out from between the two leaves, pushed through the old leaves above, out into the sunlight, where it opened out into a green leaf.

It was a long green leaf, made up of many separate leaflets, a great many pairs of them. Then it put out another and another, and you could see that it was going to be a walnut tree. If you would like to see one like it, look under the walnut trees in the spring (Fig. 7).

After the young tree had put out several leaves it took a rest, and when October came, I found it with a hood on the end of the stem.

7. LEAF OF BLACK WALNUT ABOUT ONE-HALF NATURAL SIZE.

The hood was made from leaves which did not grow long, but which remained short and dark. These were the bud scales and they covered the winter bud.

Then it dropped the leaves it had put out in the spring and passed the winter as a bare twig. In the spring it dropped the bud scales, and made some more green leaves, and then again it made a winter bud.

Each year it added a few inches to its height and a few leaves to the ends of its branches. Each year it added a layer to its bark and made new winter buds.

So it became a tall young tree, with strength to spare, and in the spring it fashioned houses for new nuts, and catkins which should shed pollen dust.

Just as the mother tree had stored food in its seed leaves, it now stored food in the leaves of its own seed children.

The tree grew tall and beautiful in its forest home. Its umbrellalike head was lifted some sixty feet into the bright sunshine. Its plumelike leaves waved in the breeze for a hundred summers more.

And then there came a change. On the edge of the forest there sprang up a little town.

The hum of the sawmill frightened away the birds. By and by the land was all cleared and the daisies ploughed under. And the tree? I suspect it passed through the sawmill.

THE WALNUT FAMILY.

The walnut tree whose story I have told is the American black walnut. It has been so highly valued for its beautiful dark wood that the forests, once very abundant in the Mississippi Valley, have almost entirely disappeared. Fortunately it is now being planted and cultivated for future use although it grows very slowly.

It is distinguished from other walnuts by its long leaf, with fifteen to twenty-three leaflets, its dark wood, and the nut which is nearly black with sharply cut ridges.

The white walnut, or butternut, is also prized for its wood which is reddish in color, but not so desirable as black walnut. It has a shorter leaf, with from nine to seventeen leaflets; the base of its fuzzy stem is shaped like a horseshoe. The nut is oblong and pointed at the tip, and the kernel is much valued.

The English, or European walnut, is frequently cultivated in the mild portions of the United States. It has short leaves with five to nine leaflets (Fig. 8); the thin-shelled nut separates easily from the husk when dry.

8. LEAF OF ENGLISH WALNUT. They are common in the market.

The hickories are closely related to the walnuts, by their leaves, flowers, and nuts with a bony partition. They are separated from the walnuts on account of the husk; the husk of the walnut is continuous, of one piece; the husk of the hickory opens by four distinct valves.

The shagbark, or hickory, is a tall, spreading tree, with bark which breaks away in long strips and has light-colored wood. The leaves have usually five leaflets which are several inches in length. The nut is thin walled, whitish and slightly flattened.

The big shellbark has a larger leaf, with from seven to nine leaflets, which are downy on the under side. The young twigs are slightly orange colored. The nut is larger and pointed at both ends.

The pecan is the species found in the South. It grows to a greater height than the northern forms. The leaves are longer, with from nine to fifteen pointed leaflets and the husk is thin, with yellowish threads.

It opens by four valves dropping the nut but not the husk. The nut is oblong, about an inch in length, smooth and thin-shelled. The kernel is sweet and of excellent flavor.

Reference:
Seed Babies. Margaret Morley.
Nuts Falling. Foster, in Child's Garden of Song.
Succession of Forest Trees. Thoreau.

THE CONE BEARERS.

At one time there was a great forest of pine trees. They covered the hillsides and the steep slopes of the mountains. They stood "spear straight" in the moss by the streams. They looked down from the cliffs where they grew tall and strong, or clung ragged and stunted to the bare rocks.

On the edge of this forest lived the Indians. Their young men grew up in the shade of the pines, and somehow they were alike.

The trees were dark and somber; they cared not for summer nor winter. Neither were the Indians merry. They were fearless and hardy; no blast was too strong and no cold too fierce.

They trapped the beaver, and followed the bear under the trees, and they listened to the winds when they whistled or moaned through the branches.

When they danced and sung round their warfires the pines echoed their voices. And so they came to feel that the trees were alive, that there was in the tree a spirit to which they could appeal. They also thought that some men had been changed into trees.

Even now there is in the Bitter Rcot Mountains a great "medicine" or "peace tree." It is a pine and stands on the boundary between two tribes. Under it they settle their disputes, and to it they bring offerings which they hang on its branches.

Shall I tell you some of the stories they used to tell about the pines?

A long time ago there were ten Indian boys living in a village. They were great friends. Every evening at dusk they would meet and dance about one of their number who was a sweet singer.

Once they wanted to have a great feast. But their parents thought it was foolish and would not give them the things for which they asked.

That night they came out and danced as usual. The singer sung more sweetly than ever before. As he sung they danced faster and faster. Then the singer rose into the air and still they whirled round and round him.

Their mothers came out and called to them to come back and they might have what they wished. Still they rose higher and higher, dancing around the singer.

Only one of them looked back and he fell to the earth and was changed into a pine tree.

And so the pine trees still tell the fate of the boys who danced away into the clouds. The trunk is the singer, and its circles of branches are the boys who danced about him.

Away up in the top of a pine tree there is a tip like a feather. This is the story they tell about it.

Three men once went to the great spirit Glooskap to ask for favors. The first was a young Indian who wore bark and fur in his moccasins in order to appear tall. He also plastered his hair high and stuck in it a turkey feather.

"What would you have?" asked Glooskap.

"I wish to be taller than any Indian in the land," said he.

Glooskap was not pleased, and turned to the second. "What will you have?" he asked.

The second wanted to live upon the earth forever that he might see its beauty.

"Grant that I may live to be very old, and that I may have good health to enjoy it," said the third.

Glooskap called his servant and told him to take the men to a hill near by and fasten their feet in the ground. This done he changed them into pine trees.

In this way each had his wish granted. If you will listen when you pass under the pines you can hear their voices and see the turkey feather in the top.

Some of the pine trees are very, very tall. Would you like to hear how they became so?

The great Manabozho had been hunting one day when he came to the edge of the forest. He saw the prince of the serpents lying on the sand by the Big-Sea-Water.

Manabozho remembered how much harm the serpents had done and so he shot a magic arrow straight to its heart and killed it. Then he turned and ran.

The serpent had given a loud cry, and the others hearing it came to him. When they saw that Manabozho had killed him, they started after him, crawling and leaping.

They went so fast that they were soon upon him and he could hear them hissing. He had run to the top of a mountain and now he had just time to climb the tree he found there. The serpents were about its base.

"Waters of Earth, rise and save me," he cried.

The waters came, roaring and splashing. They rose to the top of the mountain, they swallowed the serpents, and crept higher and higher up the tree. They came about his feet.

" Tree, Tree, stretch and save me," he cried.

The tree was a pine. It stretched and stretched until it was several times as tall as before. And still the waters rose.

They crept to his knees, to his waist, but when they reached his neck they stopped.

He called to a passing loon to dive and bring up some earth. It dived but came up dead.

Then a muskrat came floating by. Manabozho called to it, " Muskrat, bring me some dirt from the ground below the water and you shall have your choice of places on the new earth I will build."

The muskrat dived and brought up some dirt in its paws. It seemed to be dead, but Manabozho breathed into its nostrils and it came to life.

So Manabozho made a new earth and ever since the pine trees have been taller than other trees.

THE PINE FAMILY.

Almost all cone bearing trees are called pines by those who have not studied them. The pine family includes not only the true pines, but the firs and spruces, the hemlocks, larches and cedars.

They are also called " evergreens," for they do not drop their leaves as do many of the other common trees. This does not mean that the leaves never drop at all, but that they do not fall at the same time or on the approach of winter.

If you look under the trees you can always find the dried needles that have fallen. They fall from the inner and older parts of the branches.

Evergreen leaves do not look much like those of other trees; they are sometimes long and pointed like needles; they may be narrow and flat; they may look like flattened scales on the branches, or they may be short and awl-like.

Such leaves are much stiffer than other leaves and must have some way of protecting themselves against the cold. They are usually resinous, that is, there are in each leaf

1. PINE CONE.

bodies which produce a thick, sticky gum, which we call balsam. This is sometimes fragrant, as in the fir balsam.

The pines are much more like the trees that were growing on the earth at the time that the great coal beds were forming than are any of the deciduous trees. Their leaves are more like the leaves of the old club mosses.

Their cones are also somewhat like those of the ancient mosses. In this way we know that the pines are much older *in their form* than the deciduous trees.

The fruit of the pines is called a cone. You have all seen cones. They are usually round or oval in shape, and consist of a central axis, around which grow many stiff, hard, brown scales.

Sometimes these scales are thin and flat, sometimes they are thick and rough. In the pines (Fig. 1) they overlap, but in the cypresses (Fig. 11) and in the cedars their edges may fit together so that they are rather ball-like, and have hard ridges.

If you could watch a cone grow you would find that it began as a twig begins. The parts that in a twig grow into leaves, in a cone flatten out and become the scales of the cone. The seed are borne on these scales.

2. SECTION OF A SEED (MAGNIFIED).

Even in their seed the pine family are quite different from the deciduous trees. A pine nut is smooth on the outside. Cut away the shell, and the kernel looks like a small egg with a small cap on one end. That cap is always found among the cone bearers.

Now, if you cut the white kernel in two, you will find that the outside is food, and in the center of the food is a tiny little plant, which may be green at one end (Fig. 2).

This is the young pine tree, this is the part which when you plant the nut, cracks the shell, and pushes

3. NORWAY SPRUCE.

its way out. These young plants are different from all other seedlings you may find.

Instead of one seed leaf, like the corn, or two seed leaves, like the maple, there are a circle of narrow leaves, usually about eight or ten. When the young tree begins to branch, buds form in a circle, and become a circle of branches. But the middle bud is stronger than any of the others. It forms the trunk which always exceeds the branches.

4. NORWAY SPRUCE. *a*, STAMINATE CATKIN; *b*, SCALE (BOTH MAGNIFIED).

The Norway spruce is the easiest to find of this group. It is cultivated in almost all the parks of this country. It is an evergreen tree, with a straight, slender trunk and circles of slightly drooping branches.

The sprays are flattened and the stems covered with short needles of about an inch in length. The

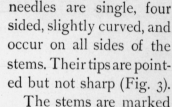

needles are single, four sided, slightly curved, and occur on all sides of the stems. Their tips are pointed but not sharp (Fig. 3). The stems are marked with c u r i o u s flat ridges or cushions from which the needles spring.

If the tree is well grown, you may find it in flower in April or May. On the under side of the sprays will be found some dull yellow catkins of about an inch in length (Fig. 4). They are not at all woolly, and consist of overlapping scales. Each scale is supplied with two pockets, from which the pollen is shed when ripe (Fig. 4, *b*).

These are the staminate catkins. The pistillate catkins or young cones are always higher up near the top of the tree. They are about an inch in length, of a deep red color, and hang down. They, too, are made of flattened scales, at the base of

5. CONES OF NORWAY SPRUCE (RE-DUCED). *a*, SCALE, SHOWING SEED.

6. SECTION OF CONE.

each scale are two tiny oval bodies which grow into seeds after they have been supplied with pollen (Fig. 5, *a*).

The mature cones are from four to six inches long, and very regular in their shape. There is a central axis upon which the bracts or scales are arranged spirally. Figure 6 shows a cut through a cone, the bracts upon either side, and the seeds as they lie upon the bracts.

Since the seed do not lie in a closed cavity, cone bearing trees are known as *Gymnosperms*, or trees with naked seed. The seed are winged, and fall out when the scales loosen in February.

The true pines have flowers very much like these but they are grouped differently. There is usually a cluster of the staminate catkins near the end of the lower branches. The young cones are higher up on older trees. They seem to take the place of a circle of young twigs on the branches.

Great Groups in the Pine Family.

I am sure you will want to be able to distinguish the best known members of the pine family. This can be easily done, if you answer the following questions.

Is your cone bearer an evergreen?

If not, it is probably a larch or the southern cypress.

If evergreen, are there some thin dry bud scales about the base of the leaves?

If so, it is a true pine. The leaves usually occur in groups of from two to five wrapped together, and the cones are thick and woody. The Scotch pine and yellow pine have the needles arranged in clusters of two. The pitch pine has the needles in groups of three. The white pines have five needles in a cluster. The bark is smooth and of a pale color (Fig. 7).

7. WHITE PINE.

Are the leaves of your evergreen single, and attached to little ridges on the stem? Do the cones droop? Then it is a spruce or a hemlock.

The spruces have the needles arranged on all sides of the stems. Each needle is a little bit four-sided. The cones fall as one piece.

The black spruce of America and the white spruce have shorter cones than the one described. The first has dark bark and small cones; the second has light green foliage and a cone about two inches long. They both grow in the northern United States and in Canada where there are large forests.

The Colorado spruce has sharp-pointed, pungent leaves and the branches incline upward.

The hemlocks differ from the spruces in that the leaves are flattened and arranged in two rows on the stems like a feather (Fig. 8). This gives the tree a dainty, feathery spray which droops decidedly. The staminate catkins are nearly round.

Are the leaves of your evergreen single, flattened,

8. HEMLOCK.

and inclined to turn upward so that the under side of the stem is nearly bare? Then you have a fir. Observe that each leaf springs from a circular disk.

The balsam firs are native Americans, and have served as Christmas trees for several centuries. The blisters upon their bark yield Canada balsam, and their leaves are very fragrant. Figure 9 represents a twig of the northern balsam fir.

The cones of the fir trees stand erect on the stems. When they open to shed the seed, the scales fall at the same time. This leaves the central axis standing. There are often conspicuous bracts between the scales.

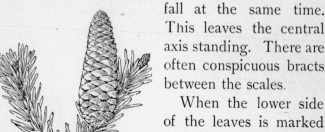

When the lower side of the leaves is marked with white, they are called silver firs. These are very handsome trees.

The cedars may puzzle you at first, but if you look at them closely, or get the cones it will not be for long.

9 NORTHERN BALSAM FIR.

The Lebanon cedars have needlelike leaves arranged in tufts.

The white cedars have flattened stems covered with four rows of overlapping scales. They are of two kinds, those having the flattened branches extending up and down the tree, from top to bottom, and those in which the branches extend around the tree.

The first are called arbor vitæ (Fig. 10). The scales of the cones overlap. The second are called cypresses (Fig. 11). The cones are round like marbles. These are very common in California.

10. ARBOR VITÆ.

11. Cypress.

The junipers, or red cedars, do not have a cone at all, but bear purple berries. The leaves are either scalelike or sharp and pointed, and the branches are horizontal.

References:

The Fir Tree. Hans Christian Andersen.

To a Pine Tree. Lowell.

Growth of the Legend. Lowell.

A Mood. Lowell

My Cathedral. Longfellow.

The Little Pine Tree. E. S. Bumstead in *Fairyland of Science.*

Three Trees. Nature in Verse.

The Little Christmas Tree. Susan Coolidge.

The Little Fir Tree. Evaleen Stein in St. Nicholas.

The Legend of Skadi. Lucy Larcom.

The Pine Forest of Monterey. Bayard Taylor.

Ariel in the Cloven Pine. Bayard Taylor.

Legends of the Algonquin Indians of New England. Leland.

THE RED MAPLE.

Good news!   Good news!

Winter is going!   Winter, with his gloomy skies and whistling winds!   Winter who gives

> The fields and the trees, so old,
> Their beards of icicles and snow.

There's not a robin to be seen, not a spring beauty peeping out of the snow, but down by the river I have found a tree, a beautiful red tree.

It blooms earlier than the pussy willows, earlier than the crocuses. Sometimes it blooms so very early that the gray old king nips its buds and turns its twigs brown.

There are no leaves yet on this tree, but you may know it by its shape, by the compact round head, low branches, sharp angles and bushy twigs. The bark is thin, a grayish brown on the trunk, red on the twigs. It is smooth above, but down below it has cracked lengthwise.

1. WINTER BUDS.

Let us see what kind of a tree it is. Here on the twigs are the scars of last year's leaves, in pairs and **V**-shaped (Fig. 1).

If there are three or four eyes in each scar, it is a maple. This one with its red twigs and flowers is the red maple. It grows wild along streams and in swamps. Sometimes we call it the swamp maple.

The flowers are these bright red tufts. The poet, Lowell, calls them the maple's "corals." There are so many of them that they color the whole tree red. You must look closely to discover that there are two kinds.

Some of them have little balls covered with yellow dust, while others have just two tiny red plumes in each flower (Figures 2 and 3).

On this tree you find a great many of the balls and only a few of the plumes; but on some of the trees you will find a great many of the plumes with but very few balls. In some families all the children are boys, in others girls, and in others there are boys and girls together, so with the maple, one tree may have balls or *stamens* alone, another plumes or *pistils*, and still another (though this kind is more rare) may have stamens and pistils together.

2. *a*. STAMINATE FLOWERS.
b. STAMINATE FLOWER
(MAGNIFIED).

Both the balls and the plumes grow in red cups. These help to keep them warm. It would not be safe for every tree to bloom at this season, but the red maple seems to be prepared for cold weather in several ways.

First, the flowers grow in tufts. That keeps out some of the wind, for they bloom just

When wild March winds on their errands sing.

Second, the buds are protected by scales. You will find them turned back just below the open flowers, but they show better in the bud, around the young flowers.

There is a brown and shiny coat of resin, a waterproof, to keep out the rain and snow. They are so small, these tiny flowers, that they do not need a waterproof for each, but are wrapped up three or four together.

Third, when the bud scales turn back, and the flowers push out on their *pedicels*, they have still two red cloaks or cups, which keep the inner parts warm. The outer of these is called a *calyx*, the inner a *corolla* (Fig. 3, *b*).

3. *a*, PISTILLATE FLOWERS; *b*, PISTILLATE FLOWER (MAGNIFIED); *c*, PISTIL (MAGNIFIED).

When the cup contains stamens, they may be from four to twelve in number, each with a tiny ball or *anther*. Each ball has four little pockets full of yellow dust, called *pollen* (Fig. 2).

When the pollen falls upon the red plumes, it pushes its way into the urn-shaped body at the base. This then begins to grow; its shoulders enlarge and each becomes a broad flat wing or sail. Such a two-winged fruit is a *samara* or key (Fig. 4).

You may remember seeing such keys late in the year when the wind carries them about, whisking them into corners, or dropping them in the shade of the mother tree.

Some day you may open one and see what is within. Carefully cut away one wall of the thickened base.

There are two little rooms, and in each one is a seed. Now cut off the seed wall also.

4. KEYS OF RED MAPLE.

What do you find? Two tiny baby maples, twins they are, all wrapped up and swung in a winged cradle!

Each one has a tiny root and two little leaves. The root works down into the soil and gathers water with its velvety root hairs. The stem pushes up in to the sunlight. The second pair of leaves differ in shape from the first or seed leaves, and the third are more perfect still (Figures 6 and 7).

5. SECTION OF KEY SHOWING PLANTLET.

All summer long the little maples grow, adding to their crown of leaves, till in the fall they may be two feet tall. Then winter comes and the cold kills them off by the hundreds.

The red maple blooms early, so that the children grow tall and strong before winter begins. The keys, falling as they do upon the wet soil of marsh and river, could not live through the winter but would decay. Fortunately the swamp maple blooms in March and drops its keys in May.

When this is done the maple has summer before it, the long, warm summer in which to work and build.

6. PLANTLET REMOVED FROM THE SEED.

After the flowers bloom the winter buds unfold. The winter buds are at the end of the twigs and are darker in color than the flower buds. They, too, are covered with scales, coated with resin, and lined with wool. There are six or eight of them.

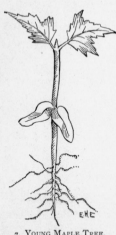

Do you see a scar just below the flower buds on either side? The flower buds grew in the axil of the lowest scale, and it has fallen away and left a scar. The first leaves are not quite perfect, but seem to be half leaf, half scale. Having been wrapped up in the bud all winter, they never recover from the effects of

7. YOUNG MAPLE TREE.

the crowded position (Fig. 8).

Spread one of the later leaves out on your hand and you will see why they are described as *palmate* and five lobed. If you look at a number you may find some with only three lobes. The margin is notched and the leaves are opposite.

When they first unfold the leaves are deep red in color. As they grow older and turn green, the maple uses them to prepare food. It takes the water from the soil and gas from the air, just such gas as you throw out of your lungs, and it mixes them there behind the green curtain.

That curtain is of wonderful material. It does not let all the light through; that which passes is of a deep green color, and it turns the gas and water into starch and sugar.

When October comes, the season for making food is over. Then the maple takes in the green curtains and

8. FROM SCALE TO BUD.

puts up some of crimson and yellow and scarlet.

This is the time when squirrels gather their nuts and farmers house their grain for winter use. The trees, too, are making ready for winter. They are storing *sap* away in the trunk.

The beautiful colors are also useful. Though trees need sunlight, it may sometimes be too strong.

The food, which is carried in the sap, might easily be hurt by the sunlight, but the bright colors turn back a part of the light, so that the food reaches the trunk in safety.

The young leaves are also red, until they begin to produce the leaf green which they use in making the food.

When the food is safely stored, the tree has no further use for the leaves. They turn brown and fall to the ground. But they are not altogether lost, for the soil they fall upon is richer for the shower of leaves.

There is something else which a maple makes during the sunny summer. It is *wood*, wood in which to keep warm when the wintry winds are blowing.

This wood is somewhat pink in color and is often used to make furniture, gunstocks and other things. One kind, the "bird's eye maple" is very handsome. You may look for it yourself some day. The wood extends out into the bark in very many minute prickles. When this is cut and polished, it is found to be marked with many circular grains, the "bird's eyes."

Another kind is the "curly maple." The woody fibers, which are usually quite straight, are sometimes wavy. When such wood is polished it shows lights and shades like the folds of a satin gown, and is called "curly" maple.

Did you ever think how long it takes a tree to build its house of wood? If you were small enough to go through all its rooms, you would find it a perfect palace. Every year new rooms are added, always between the wood and the bark. In this way a ring is added each year.

We can tell the age of a tree by the number of rings in its wood. If there are a hundred rings, the tree is a hundred years old.

Such a tree has many friends. It is fixed in a single place, but the winds and birds can come and go.

The wind is a family friend of long standing, one that has been trusted by the family for generations. He carries the pollen from tree to tree, and starts the children out into the world. He also drives the clouds to the hills, and cools the leaves when the air is hot.

As for others, the shyest birds sing in its branches; it shares their joys and sorrows, and protects them with its shade. Another good friend is Jack Frost, who warns it when winter is coming, that it may be ready.

But Jack is not the maple's friend alone; he does many kind things for nature's other children. The wild geese must be driven southward; the gray partridge must be warned to put on her snow white feathers; he whispers to the brown bear to find a hollow tree, and invites the red squirrel to North Hollow when he opens the farmer's chestnuts.

How would you like to live a life like that of the maple? You could never leave your house at all, but it would be warm and comfortable during the cold, hard winters. Sometimes the melting snows would swell the streams in the spring and would wash all the earth from your roots; or the worms might eat the leaves from your branches; the sugar man might steal your sap; or the lumber man take your house. But think of the long days of sunshine, under blue skies, when you could wave your leaves in the breeze; of the cool showers, and of the lovely nights with the moon and stars and crooning birds.

NATIVE MAPLES.

The red maple is found in the northern and eastern parts of the United States. It is often planted along streets or in parks, but grows wild only in river bottoms and swampy places.

It has a great many relatives which you may meet and which you may know by their palmate, opposite leaves, and the two-winged fruit, although they may differ in other respects.

The silver maple is a tall tree with a pale bark, which flakes off in thin sheets. Like the red maple, it blooms early, but its tufts of flowers are much thicker, and its buds more numerous. When the flowers come out, there is a single hairy green cup to keep the inner parts warm. Its leaves are silvery below with deep, sharp notches.

This tree is widely planted for it grows very rapidly. The wood is soft, and when burned does not give much heat.

The sugar maple is another relative, and is well known for its sweet sap. It does not bloom early. The flowers and leaves come out together, and the keys are not shed until October. They fall on dry ground, however, and the seed leaves are filled with starch, so they wait till spring before they start to grow. The flower has a long pedicel and there is but one cup. The leaves are nearly round, with a few large, blunt notches. It is known as the "hard" maple, for the wood is tough and close grained.

9. MOUNTAIN MAPLE
(REDUCED).

The striped maple has light green bark, striped with dark lines. The wood is hard and fine, but it does not grow very tall unless it is grafted upon a young tree of another kind of maple, when it may become sixty or seventy feet high.

The mountain maple is shrubby also. Its leaves appear before the flowers, which occur in a long spike at the ends of the twigs. There are large numbers of keys in a cluster (Fig. 9).

The great-leaved maple, of California, has leaves which are often a foot broad and the scar is marked with seven eyes. Another, the vine maple of Oregon, forms dense clumps. It divides near the base and the long branches bend over by their own weight, taking root where they touch the ground. There are also many maples which have been brought over from Europe.

The box elder closely resembles the maple, but its stamens and pistils do not occur on the same tree; its leaves consist of from three to five leaflets.

References:

Under the October Maples. Lowell.
The Maple. Lowell.
The Trees. Lucy Larcom
October. Lucy Larcom.
Indian Summer Reverie. Lowell.

FORESTS AND THEIR PRESERVATION.

The forests of America have been rapidly depleted in the past century. At one time they were thought to be inexhaustible. This has been found not to be the case. The young timber does not grow so rapidly as to replace that which has been removed.

This is in part due to the growth of industry and in part to the wasteful use of trees.

The industries depending upon the products of trees are so numerous and the necessity for renewing the trees so self-evident that the government has been obliged to study the subject thoroughly.

Large quantities of timber are used in building; manufacturing, fencing, for railroad ties, and fuel; the bark is used in the tanning of leather; turpentine, pitches, and sugar are derived by tapping the trees.

The most considerable waste is due to forest fires, and the ruthless cutting of timber on the public lands. Charcoal is frequently burned without any attempt to preserve the gases which would be of value for illuminating purposes.

One of the first effects of removing the forests in a neighborhood has been the necessity of bringing in lumber from other localities; this increases its price.

It is, however, in its final effects upon a country that clearing the hills has proved most detrimental.

It has been found that cleared districts are not so warm in winter as before the hills were bared. This has caused a failure in crops formerly successful.

In northern Illinois, the climate was so altered by the removal of woods that the peach crops were seriously injured. Winter wheat was killed in open fields, but was successful where protected by the woods.

Thus in winter the trees break the winds and moderate the cold; in summer they reduce the heat, and lessen the danger from storms. Since the removal of trees many localities, which were formerly free from storms, are visited by storms of great violence.

Forests produce conditions leading to rain. The evaporation from the soil and leaves cools the atmosphere and tends to precipitate the moisture. This rain does not run off at once as it often does in the open field.

The ground being mellow and loose, it sinks and is gradually fed out to springs and streams. Snows falling in the forest melt but slowly and so a supply of water is maintained for the summer.

Where woods have been replanted, the irregular rainfalls and frequent droughts observed since clearing, have disappeared, and more favorable conditions prevail.

Birds, too, are wont to nest in woods. They desert the clearings in such numbers that crops are injured by the insects they used to destroy.

It is for these reasons that the government encourages the planting of trees. It has made favorable terms to settlers who cultivate trees. Various states are doing what they can to remedy the evils brought about by the indiscriminate cutting of trees.

The strictest laws are issued to control the setting of fires in the woods, and to prevent their spreading. The treeless character of the prairie regions is thought to be due to the burning of the trees by the Indians.

The old timber culture laws were not an entire success for trees were planted without care and without regard to their adaptability. This is now remedied so far as possible. Investigation has decided which trees are suitable in certain localities.

There are in almost every place some parts which would be more profitable in trees than in the usual crop. But they must be cared for, they can not be neglected as they have been in times past.

Trees are also planted largely as wind breaks in prairie regions, and some experiments have been made to redeem certain beach tracts from the encroaching sands by planting trees which will resist the winds.

To prevent floods and shortage of water during the summer, the government has made laws which

are designed to stop the cutting of trees upon
public lands except under definite regulations.
These look to the preservation of the young trees
and the ultimate recovering of the hills with a
growth of trees.

References:

Reports upon Forestry. Department of Agriculture.
Forests of North America. C. S. Sargent. (Government
Report.) This gives fine maps of the wooded districts in each
state, with the character of the trees found in each.

Nature Readers

FOR ELEMENTARY GRADES

STORIES OF ANIMAL LIFE
By CHARLES F. HOLDER, LL.D., Author of " Elements
of Zoölogy " . . . . 60 cents

This book is intended to serve either as a first book on Zoölogy or
as a supplementary reader. The author has aimed to create in young
students an enthusiastic interest in Nature Study by presenting some
of the most remarkable phases of animal life. Under the guise of
stories he has brought out many facts not generally available and covering a wide field.

SHORT STORIES OF OUR SHY NEIGHBORS
By Mrs. M. A. B. KELLY . . . . . . 50 cents

This book furnishes children with entertaining and instructive
reading in the field of Natural History. It tells about the birds, insects,
and other living creatures that dwell near us and yet are oftentimes
strangers, and unnoticed save by the closest observers. It does this in
the form of stories, written in such a pleasing and attractive style, and
so copiously illustrated, as to deeply interest the young reader, and
awaken in his mind an enthusiasm and desire to become better acquainted
with the wonders of the animate world.

PLANTS AND THEIR CHILDREN
By Mrs. WILLIAM STARR DANA.   Illustrated by Alice
Josephine Smith . . . . 65 cents

A series of easy lessons on the Wonders of Plant Life written in
such a charming manner as to make them as entertaining for children as
stories, and their study a pleasure instead of a task. These studies in
nature are not only interesting and instructive in themselves but they
teach the most important lessons a child can learn,—to see, to think, and
to observe for himself, and thus to become an intelligent student of
nature.

OUTDOOR STUDIES
By JAMES G. NEEDHAM . . . . . . 40 cents

Intended to supply a series of lessons in Nature Study suitable for
pupils in the intermediate or grammar grades and designed for pupils of
some years' experience and some training in observation. The book
may be used as a guide for field work as well as a reader in Nature Study.
The insight thus gained into the secrets of nature will pave the way for
more intelligent and profitable text-book study and for laboratory work
in the higher grades.

*Copies of any of the above books will be sent, prepaid, to any address
on receipt of the price by the Publishers :*

American Book Company

New York   •   Cincinnati   •   Chicago
(22)

Natural History Readers

McGUFFEY'S FAMILIAR ANIMALS AND THEIR WILD KINDRED

> For the Third Reader Grade. Cloth, 12mo. 208 pages.
> Illustrated . . . . 50 cents

McGUFFEY'S LIVING CREATURES OF WATER, LAND, AND AIR

> For the Fourth Reader Grade. Cloth, 12mo. 208 pages.
> Illustrated . . . . 50 cents

The object of McGuffey's Natural History Readers is to furnish children, both at home and in school, interesting and instructive reading, arranged and graded for reading lessons. While no attempt is made to teach science, the descriptions of animal habits and characteristics will stimulate a love of nature, and of science, the interpreter of nature.

The first book of the series confines its subjects to mammals because the facts connected with this class are apparent and are more easily comprehended. The second book enters the field of the lower group of animal life, where the facts while more remote from ordinary view are even more interesting. The illustrations in both books are numerous and in the highest degree accurate and helpful, being mostly by artists whose study and practice have made them specialists in particular departments of animal drawing.

Copies of McGuffey's Natural History Readers will be sent, prepaid, to any address on receipt of the price by the Publishers:

American Book Company

New York • Cincinnati • Chicago

Supplementary Reading

JOHONNOT'S HISTORICAL READERS

SIX BOOKS. 12MO. ILLUSTRATED.

Grandfather's Stories. 140 pages	27 cents
Stories of Heroic Deeds. 150 pages	30 cents
Stories of Our Country. 207 pages	40 cents
Stories of Other Lands. 232 pages	40 cents
Stories of the Olden Time. 254 pages	54 cents
Ten Great Events in History. 264 pages	54 cents

JOHONNOT'S NATURAL HISTORY READERS

SIX BOOKS. 12MO. ILLUSTRATED.

Book of Cats and Dogs. 96 pages	17 cents
Friends in Feathers and Fur. 140 pages . . .	30 cents
Neighbors with Wings and Fins. 229 pages . . .	40 cents
Some Curious Flyers, Creepers, and Swimmers. 224 pages	40 cents
Neighbors with Claws and Hoofs. 256 pages . . .	54 cents
Glimpses of the Animate World. 414 pages . . .	$1.00

These books are admirably adapted for use as supplementary readers. Each series contains a full course of graded lessons for reading on instructive topics, written in a style that is of the most fascinating interest to children and young people, at the same time training them to habits of observation and storing their minds with valuable information. Each book is fully illustrated in an artistic and attractive manner.

Copies of any of the above books will be sent, prepaid, to any address on receipt of the price by the Publishers :

American Book Company

New York • Cincinnati • Chicago
(20)

Advanced Supplementary Reading

Rolfe's Tales of Chivalry $0.36
Rolfe's Tales from English History 36
Rolfe's Tales from Scottish History 50
Guerber's Story of the Thirteen Colonies 65
Guerber's Story of the Great Republic 65
Guerber's Story of the English 65
Guerber's Story of the Greeks 60
Guerber's Story of the Romans 60
Guerber's Story of the Chosen People 60
Clarke's Story of Troy 60
Clarke's Story of Ulysses 60
Clarke's Story of Aeneas 45
Clarke's Story of Caesar 45
Shepherd's Historical Readings 1.00
Skinner's Readings in Folk-Lore 1.00
Skinner's Schoolmaster in Literature 1.40
Skinner's Schoolmaster in Comedy and Satire 1.40
Seven American Classics (Standard Series) 50
Seven British Classics (Standard Series) 50
Cathcart's Literary Reader 1.15
McCaskey's Lincoln Literary Collection 1.00
Johonnot's Geographical Reader 1.00
Johonnot's Glimpses of the Animate World 1.00
Cooper's Animal Life 1.25
Holder's Stories of Animal Life 60
Herrick's Chapters on Plant Life 60
Treat's Home Studies in Nature 90

Copies sent, prepaid, to any address on receipt of the price.

American Book Company

New York   •   Cincinnati   •   Chicago
(24)